Reading Comprehension

Book 1

Jo Browning Wroe
David Lambert

Permission to photocopy

This book contains worksheets which may be reproduced by photocopier or other means for use by the purchaser. This permission is granted on the understanding that these copies will be used within the educational establishment of the purchaser. This book and all its contents remain copyright. Copies may be made without reference to the publisher or the licensing scheme for the making of photocopies operated by the Publishers' Licensing Agency.

The rights of Jo Browning Wroe and David Lambert to be identified as authors of this work have been asserted by them in accordance with sections 77 and 78 of the Copyright, Designs and Patents Act 1988.

Reading Comprehension Book 1
LL05039
ISBN 1 85503 362 3
© Jo Browning Wroe and David Lambert
Illustrations by Mike Taylor, Felicity House and David Pattison
All rights reserved
First published 2003
Reprinted 2003 (June), 2004 (twice)

Printed in the UK for LDA
LDA, Abbeygate House, East Road, Cambridge, CB1 1DB UK

Contents

Teacher's notes

Each book in the LDA Reading Comprehension series provides 33 stimulating photocopiable comprehension activities for the children you teach. In line with the National Literacy Strategy, the books present a wide variety of text types, including newspaper articles, poetry, dialogue, prose, instructions, charts and tables, letters, guidebook information and journal entries.

The activities are graded so that you will find a general trend of increasing conceptual complexity or discoursal organisation within the texts as you move through each section.

The four skill areas
To develop and hone your pupils' skills in four crucial areas of reading comprehension, the activities are grouped under the following headings:

Getting the main idea
In these activities, the pupils' overall grasp of the text is tested. To answer the questions, they are required to use their understanding of the text's main theme, argument or development.

Making inferences
The questions in this section encourage the pupils to make connections between the discrete elements embedded in the text. Pupils must choose, from a range of possibilities, the answer that is most *likely* to be true.

Noting details
Here, pupils are invited to scan the text for information and to retrieve discrete facts, for example an opening time, a date, or a figure. Occasionally, a more systematic reading is required to grasp the relationship between facts embedded in the text.

Using context clues
The questions in these activities encourage pupils to be sleuths, searching the textual environment for *clues* in order to select the most appropriate words or phrases to fill the blanks and complete the passage.

The questions
For each activity there are five questions that relate directly to the text. In most cases these are multiple choice and pupils simply have to circle the letters to indicate their answers. For the Noting details activities, pupils are required to write in their own answers.

At the end of each activity, there is a sixth, open-ended extension question. This is designed to encourage further reading, research, reflection or creativity on the same topic or a related one. These questions aim to personalise the text, making the issues raised within it relevant to the reader. There are three types of extension question:

Ask yourself
These questions tend to have an ethical slant and seek to develop pupils' critical thinking skills. For example, after an information text about the platypus:

Probably your only chance to see animals such as the platypus or the kangaroo is at the zoo. What do you think about keeping such animals in captivity? Explain the reason for your answer.

Find out for yourself
These questions put the pupils in charge of their learning, inviting them to find out more about a subject. This might be done in a number of different ways, for example by using books, searching on the Web or asking people questions. It is usually left to the pupil to identify their own sources of reference, as each of these questions is very

uch a point of departure, not an end in self. For example, following an article bout skipping:

Vrite down any skipping rhymes you know. y to find some more words of skipping ymes, either from your own area or from ther parts of the country. What differences e there?

xpress yourself
hese questions encourage pupils to respond haginatively and creatively to the texts ey have read. They might be asked to rite prose or poetry or to draw, design or ake something. For example:

ake up your own fable about a wise nimal. Think about which animals are hought of as wise and why that might be.

ow do I use the book?
hese Reading Comprehension books are tended to be a flexible teaching resource use in the way that best enhances the arning going on in your classroom. The ctivities will fit well into the small group ction of the literacy hour, but this is by no eans the only appropriate context for the aterial. At the beginning of a school year, r example, they could be used as a tool to ssess your pupils' level of comprehension nd to find if there are particular areas of eakness which can then be addressed.

he texts should take no longer than 10 inutes to read and the questions no more an another 10 minutes to complete, lthough this will vary greatly from pupil to upil.

some circumstances, it may be beneficial r pupils to tackle the activities in pairs. In is way, less able pupils who lack onfidence can provide each other with upport as they read and then answer the uestions.

There might also be occasions when it is helpful for a pupil to have access to the answers, in order to check their own work.

Answers
An answer key is provided at the back of the book on page 64.

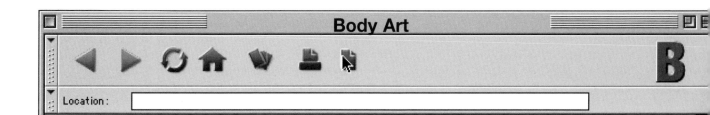

BODY ART

You might think that tattoos and body transfers are a modern idea. In fact, body art has been practised all over the world for thousands of years.

One of the oldest and safest known ways of painting on your skin is to use a natural dye called henna. Natural henna is a powder made by grinding the leaves of the henna plant. The powder can be mixed to a paste. If you put the paste on your skin it will leave a dark orange colour which will stay for three to four weeks and gradually fade away.

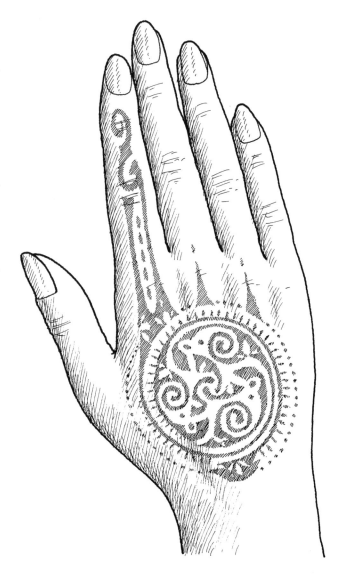

Today you can buy henna in tubes in lots of different colours. Any product called black henna is not real henna but a man-made product. The chemicals in it may harm your skin.

Body Art

Read the text carefully and circle the best ending for each sentence.

1. Body art is
   a) just for children.
   b) a modern idea.
   c) practised all over the world.

2. Natural henna comes from
   a) the seeds of the henna plant.
   b) the leaves of the henna plant.
   c) the roots of the henna plant.

3. After three to four weeks, henna painting
   a) gradually fades away.
   b) turns black.
   c) burns your skin.

4. If you use natural henna from the plant,
   a) your skin will be dark orange.
   b) your skin will go powdery.
   c) your skin will smell of oranges.

5. Black henna is
   a) good for your skin.
   b) better than orange henna.
   c) manufactured from chemicals.

Express yourself
Draw a design that could go on someone's arm.

Tricks and Illusions

A magic trick makes something that is impossible look possible. It is an illusion. A good magician makes a difficult trick look easy and natural. People like to watch magic. Many think that if they watch closely enough, they will be able to see how it is done.

Professional magicians have a code of honour, which means they do not tell people how each other's tricks are done. Some tricks are so good that even other magicians cannot work out how they are done.

Anyone can learn a few magic tricks. Simple illusions can be learned from a book. You do not need to buy special equipment. Many tricks use playing cards and coins.

There are other kinds of tricks. Escapologists, for example, escape from being tied up with chains, ropes and locks. This can be very dangerous and requires years of training. The escapologist needs to be fit, agile and have lots of nerve.

Tricks and Illusions

Read the text carefully and circle the best ending for each sentence.

 A magic trick
a) makes something impossible look possible.
b) makes something possible look impossible.
c) is impossible to do.

 Some people think if they watch a trick closely,
a) the magician will make a mistake.
b) they will see how it is done.
c) the trick will look easier.

 Professional magicians have a code of honour, which means
a) the way tricks are done is kept secret from other people.
b) they do not talk to each other.
c) they do not show their tricks to anyone at all.

 To do simple magic tricks,
a) you need special equipment.
b) you need years of training.
c) you can use playing cards, or coins.

 An escapologist
a) performs dangerous tricks.
b) only pretends to be in danger.
c) is always nervous.

Find out for yourself
Find out about the world's famous escapologists
and the amazing feats they performed.

Under the Bed

'Help! There's a horrid creature under Anna's bed!' yelled Ben, as he got up off the floor and hid behind the chair.

'You're right,' said Anna, pulling a scary face. 'It's mean and smelly and only comes out at night when we're all asleep.'

'I don't want it to be there,' cried Ben, who was only three, 'Mum! Come and get the monster from under Anna's bed.'

Mum hurried into the room. 'What on earth is going on?' she said, looking at her daughter angrily. She knelt next to Anna's bed and looked under it.

'You're right, Ben. There is a smelly thing under Anna's bed, but you don't have to worry about it.'

'Why not?' he said, peeping from behind the chair.

'Because Anna's going to put it in the wash. Aren't you, Anna?'

'Yes, Mum,' she said, as she knelt down and pulled out the old sock!

Under the Bed

Read the text carefully and circle the best ending for each sentence.

 The story is about a girl who
a) collects monsters under her bed.
b) teases her younger brother.
c) has socks that come to life at night.

 Anna's brother hides behind
a) the bed.
b) his mother.
c) a chair.

 Anna tells Ben that the monster comes out when they are
a) asleep.
b) afraid.
c) away.

 When Mum comes into the room, she is
a) scared of the monster.
b) cross with Anna.
c) looking for a sock.

 Mum tells Anna to put the sock
a) with the dirty washing.
b) in the bath.
c) in a cage.

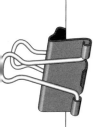

Express yourself

When you were younger, were you ever frightened of something that turned out to be harmless? Write about it.

Yo-yos

Messing around with a yo-yo is a great pastime enjoyed by kids and adults. Some people can do tricks with them. Yo-yo tricks have some odd names, such as 'Walk the Dog', 'Eiffel Tower' and 'Split the Atom'.

As far as we know, the yo-yo was invented in China, as much as 3,000 years ago. The first yo-yos consisted of two discs carved from ivory. A silk cord was wound around a peg that joined the two discs.

When the yo-yo became popular in Europe, it had several different names. The English called it a 'quiz', and the French referred to it as a 'bandalore'. Many of them were decorated with jewels and painted with beautiful patterns.

Did you know...?
Centuries ago, people took the basic idea of a yo-yo to help them hunt animals. They used large wooden discs with strong rope to catch animals by their legs.

Today, yo-yos are played with all over the world. Some are plain and simple; others have very elaborate designs and can cost a lot of money. It looks as if this old favourite will be around for many more years to come.

Yo-yos

Read the text carefully and circle the best ending for each sentence.

 1. A yo-yo is a toy that
a) only children play with.
b) only adults play with.
c) both adults and children play with.

 2. 'Walk the Dog' is a type of
a) yo-yo.
b) trick.
c) person.

 3. We think the first yo-yo was made in
a) China.
b) France.
c) Europe.

 4. Hunters used a type of yo-yo to
a) catch animals by the legs.
b) hit animals on the head.
c) swing animals round.

 5. It seems that yo-yos
a) are not very popular.
b) will soon disappear.
c) are here to stay.

Find out for yourself

Find out what other toys have been around for hundreds of years and are still played with today.

Red Kangaroo
Macropus rufus

Kangaroos can jump along at over 30 miles an hour. This is possible because of their powerful hind legs, large feet and sturdy tail, which helps them to balance.

Although they are well suited for jumping, a kangaroo's legs are not very good for walking. Kangaroos cannot move each back leg on its own, unless they are swimming.

There are about 50 different species of kangaroo, all living in Australia or New Guinea. Kangaroos do not eat meat; they are all herbivores.

Kangaroos are marsupials, so the female has a deep pouch in which she holds her baby. When a baby kangaroo (known as a joey) is first born, it is blind, bald and weighs less than 1 gram.

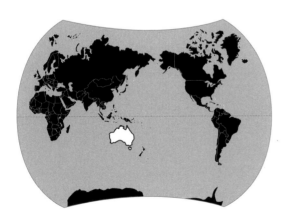

Even though it looks completely helpless, it climbs up its mother's front to the opening of the pouch and crawls in. Once inside, it can feed on its mother's milk. When the joey has grown bigger, has fur and can see, it comes out into the world. However, it still returns to its mother's pouch to sleep and travel in until it is quite well grown.

Walchester Zoo

Red Kangaroo

Read the text carefully and circle the best ending for each sentence.

 1 Kangaroos use their large tails to help them
a) balance.
b) jump.
c) race other kangaroos.

 2 Kangaroos can only use their back legs separately if they are
a) hopping.
b) walking.
c) swimming.

3 There are
a) only a few different kinds of kangaroo.
b) many different kinds of kangaroo.
c) some kangaroos that eat meat.

 4 A female kangaroo's pouch is
a) on her front.
b) called her joey.
c) where she keeps her food.

 5 When the joey is older, it still uses the pouch for
a) hiding.
b) sleeping and travelling.
c) storing its toys.

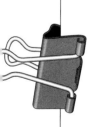

Express yourself

Write a poem or a description, imagining you are a kangaroo who loves to leap. Describe how it feels to go so fast and high.

Merlin's Treasures

One of the most famous magicians must be Merlin, from the legend of King Arthur and the Knights of the Round Table. He had many magical treasures which were used to help King Arthur.

‡ A sword that bursts into flames if any man except its owner tries to use it.

‡ A drinking horn that fills itself with whatever drink you desire.

‡ A chariot that will carry you wherever you want to go.

‡ A whetstone which sharpens a brave man's sword, but blunts the sword of a coward.

‡ A plate that brings you whatever kind of food you would like to eat.

‡ A cloak that keeps the wearer warm, even in freezing weather.

‡ A cauldron that cooks only the food of a brave man.

Merlin's Treasures

Read the text carefully and circle the best ending for each sentence.

① Merlin was a
   a) king.
   b) knight.
   c) magician.

② Merlin used his magic to
   a) help King Arthur.
   b) become a Knight of the Round Table.
   c) win treasures.

③ Merlin's sword would burst into flames if
   a) the owner tried to use it.
   b) anyone except the owner tried to use it.
   c) it was very cold.

④ Who could sharpen his sword on Merlin's whetstone?
   a) A coward.
   b) Someone who was hungry.
   c) A brave man.

⑤ When would you want to use Merlin's cloak?
   a) When it is extremely cold.
   b) When it is very hot.
   c) When you are afraid.

Express yourself

Imagine you are King Arthur. Choose one of the treasures in the passage and write a story about how it helped you in your adventures. If you don't know very much about King Arthur, try to find out more before you write your story.

Reptile Relatives

Do you know the difference between crocodiles and alligators? Is one more dangerous than the other?

Both of these reptiles can grow to over 4 metres long, but crocodiles weigh less so they can move faster. Both have webbed feet, rough skin, and short strong legs. Like all reptiles, they are both cold blooded.

To see one of the main differences between crocodiles and alligators, you have to look at them quite close to, with their mouths shut. When a crocodile closes its mouth, a sharp tooth sticks up outside its upper jaw on each side. When the alligator closes its mouth, no teeth can be seen. Also, an alligator's nose is shorter and rounder than a crocodile's.

Both alligators and crocodiles are dangerous. Never get too close to either!

Reptile Relatives

Read the text carefully and circle the best ending for each sentence.

 This piece is about the differences between
a) alligators and crocodiles.
b) alligators and reptiles.
c) crocodiles and reptiles.

 Crocodiles can move faster than alligators because they
a) have slightly longer legs.
b) are not as heavy.
c) have webbed feet.

 To notice the difference between a crocodile and an alligator you would need to see them with their
a) eyes closed.
b) mouths open.
c) mouths closed.

 When alligators close their mouths
a) they cannot breathe.
b) you can see their teeth.
c) you cannot see their teeth.

 A crocodile's nose is
a) longer than an alligator's.
b) shorter than an alligator's.
c) the same length as an alligator's.

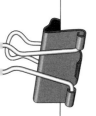

Find out for yourself

See if you can find out any more about alligators and crocodiles. Put the main differences into a list or a table.

A Peeling Poem

'It's hard being an ape in love,' moaned Chichi the chimpanzee.

'Why, Chichi?' asked his friend Polo. 'Being in love is wonderful! The world becomes more beautiful, the flowers are brighter, the air is …'

'All right, all right, I get the point,' said Chichi. 'It's hard, because the one I'm in love with doesn't even know I exist. She never smiles when I do somersaults or funny faces. She doesn't even laugh when I pretend to slip on a banana skin.'

'You need to show her how you feel. Open your heart and she won't be able to resist you.'

'That's all very well,' said Chichi, rolling his eyes. 'But how?'

'Write her a poem. It never fails,' said Polo as he gambolled off home.

That night Chichi ate a banana and wrote a poem on the skin.

> *Roses are red,*
> *Bananas are yellow.*
> *You a-peel to me –*
> *Can I be your fellow?*

A Peeling Poem

Read the text carefully and circle the best ending for each sentence.

 Chichi
   a) is in love, and excited.
   b) is in love, but unhappy.
   c) is in love, but angry.

2 Polo
   a) thinks he is an expert on love.
   b) has never been in love.
   c) doesn't like being in love.

3 Chichi has tried to impress the chimp he loves
   a) by being romantic.
   b) by being polite.
   c) by being funny.

4 Polo thinks that Chichi should be more
   a) romantic.
   b) silly.
   c) polite.

5 Chichi
   a) ignores Polo's advice.
   b) takes Polo's advice.
   c) gives Polo advice.

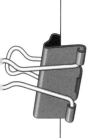

Express yourself

Pretend you are an animal and write a Valentine poem in the same style as Chichi's. For example, you could pretend to be an elephant and write:

> Roses are red,
> Peanuts are brown.
> I love your big ears –
> They're the best in town!

A GOOD DAY FOR THE PRINCESS

The beautiful young princess left the castle and wandered down to the pond. You wouldn't have known she was crying unless you were very close to her. Silent tears rolled down her rosy cheeks.

Even though it was winter, when she reached the water's edge she took off her satin shoes and silk socks and stepped barefoot into the pond.

Through her watery eyes she saw a little frog come hopping across a lily pad. She sat on the grass, her feet still in the water, and looked into his emerald face. Quick as a flash, the frog hopped onto a rock next to her and kissed her cheek. There was a popping noise and a puff of lilac smoke. Now, sitting on the grass where the princess had been, there was a frog.

Of course, if you understood frog-speak, you would have heard the princess frog thanking her prince for breaking the evil spell and turning her back into a frog forever.

A Good Day for the Princess

Read the text carefully and circle the best ending for each sentence.

 1 This story
    a) is very predictable.
    b) has a surprise ending.
    c) is a well-known tale.

 2 Stepping barefoot into the pond was
    a) a strange thing for the princess to do.
    b) what we expected the princess to do.
    c) a scary thing for the princess to do.

 3 The word 'emerald' to describe the frog makes you think that
although he is a frog, he is also
    a) rich.
    b) a prince.
    c) rather beautiful.

 4 When the frog saw the princess, he
    a) wanted to cast an evil spell on her.
    b) knew she was a frog princess.
    c) knew she was good at spells.

 5 The pond must have been
    a) the frog princess's home.
    b) full of magic frogs.
    c) surprisingly warm for the middle of winter.

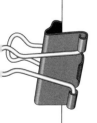

Express yourself

Tell the same story, but from the point of view of
either the frog or the princess.

Lucy and Tom

'You can't catch me!' shouted Lucy, looking Tom right in the eyes.

'Who says I want to catch you anyway?' said Tom. He was cross because he knew she was right. He was bigger, stronger and older, but there was no way he could catch Lucy. Trying to look as if he didn't care, he held his head high and stalked out of the room.

Lucy was thrilled. She used to be so scared of him, but now she knew he couldn't hurt her, she loved to tease him.

From where she was, Lucy could see into the kitchen. Mum was giving Tom his tea. She laughed when she remembered how she used to worry that Tom would eat *her* for tea. She knew that in a moment, Mum would come through into the living room and drop some delicious flakes of fish food into her tank. She had a good life!

Lucy and Tom

Read the text carefully and circle the best answer to each question.

 Tom
   a) wants to catch Lucy but can't.
   b) doesn't want to catch Lucy.
   c) is worried Lucy will catch him.

 Tom walks out of the room because
   a) he is hungry.
   b) he wants to play with Mum.
   c) he wants Lucy to think he doesn't care.

 Lucy
   a) knows that she has annoyed Tom.
   b) is afraid of Tom.
   c) wants Tom to catch her.

 When Lucy sees Tom getting his tea,
   a) she is afraid.
   b) she knows she will get hers soon.
   c) she wants some of Tom's food.

 Which of these statements is correct?
   a) Tom is a boy and Lucy is a girl.
   b) Lucy is a cat and Tom is a fish.
   c) Tom is a cat and Lucy is a fish.

Express yourself
Rewrite this story from Tom's point of view.

We Are Not Amused

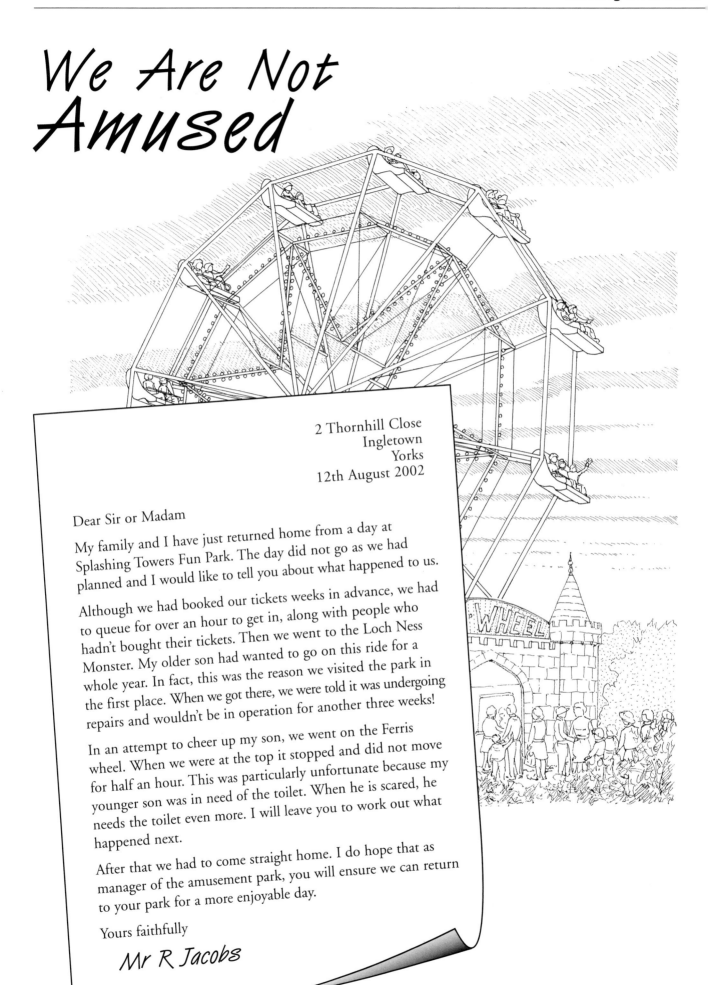

2 Thornhill Close
Ingletown
Yorks
12th August 2002

Dear Sir or Madam

My family and I have just returned home from a day at
Splashing Towers Fun Park. The day did not go as we had
planned and I would like to tell you about what happened to us.

Although we had booked our tickets weeks in advance, we had
to queue for over an hour to get in, along with people who
hadn't bought their tickets. Then we went to the Loch Ness
Monster. My older son had wanted to go on this ride for a
whole year. In fact, this was the reason we visited the park in
the first place. When we got there, we were told it was undergoing
repairs and wouldn't be in operation for another three weeks!

In an attempt to cheer up my son, we went on the Ferris
wheel. When we were at the top it stopped and did not move
for half an hour. This was particularly unfortunate because my
younger son was in need of the toilet. When he is scared, he
needs the toilet even more. I will leave you to work out what
happened next.

After that we had to come straight home. I do hope that as
manager of the amusement park, you will ensure we can return
to your park for a more enjoyable day.

Yours faithfully

Mr R Jacobs

We Are Not Amused

Read the text carefully and circle the best answer to each question.

 1 The Jacobs family
a) had not planned to go to the amusement park.
b) had planned the day in advance.
c) were very disorganised.

 2 The Loch Ness Monster was
a) a ride.
b) an animal.
c) a film.

 3 When the Jacobs got to the Loch Ness Monster,
a) they rode on it for 3 weeks.
b) they had to queue for a long time.
c) they couldn't go on it.

 4 What happened to the younger Jacobs boy on the Ferris wheel?
a) He fell asleep.
b) He wet himself.
c) He enjoyed waiting at the top.

 5 Mr Jacobs hopes the manager will
a) give them free tickets to go back another day.
b) give them their money back.
c) buy them tickets for a different amusement park.

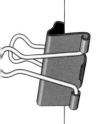

Ask yourself

Do you think it is right to complain if you do not get what you expected? What do you think makes a good complaint? How can you make a complaint so that people are likely to take notice?

Surprise

Ruby's sister Alice had broken her arm. Ruby wanted to make her a surprise treat for lunch. This is what she did.

She dropped red cubes into a bowl. Then she boiled the kettle and poured the water into the bowl. She stirred it for a few minutes until all the cubes had dissolved and the liquid was a rich red colour. Finally, Ruby topped up the bowl with cold water and put it in the fridge.

She knew she had to wait for at least an hour until the treat would be ready. All she had to do now was make sure Alice didn't open the fridge.

Surprise

Read the text carefully and circle the best answer to each question.

 Why did Ruby want to make a surprise for Alice?
a) She was cross with her.
b) She felt sorry for her.
c) She was hungry.

 What did Ruby make for Alice?
a) Ice cream.
b) Jam.
c) Jelly.

 What flavour did Ruby probably make?
a) Strawberry.
b) Lime.
c) Orange.

 Lunchtime must have been
a) less than an hour away.
b) more than an hour away.
c) exactly an hour away.

 Why didn't Ruby want Alice to open the fridge?
a) Alice wasn't supposed to eat while she had a broken arm.
b) The recipe wouldn't work.
c) It would spoil the surprise.

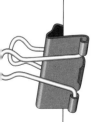

Express yourself

What was the best surprise you have ever had?
Explain who planned the surprise and how they kept
it secret from you.

A Closer Look at Skipping

PEOPLE tend to think of skipping as a game played by girls rather than by boys. However, you might be surprised to know that until around 1900, the opposite was true. The rules then were quite simple: whoever skipped for the longest was the winner.

From the beginning of the last century, skipping began to be played with songs or chanted rhymes. The same songs have been used for many years, although the exact words and tunes have varied over time. A song or chant may also be slightly different in various parts of the country.

Skipping ropes are found in playgrounds across the world, but kids are not the only skippers. Skipping is such good exercise that athletes and boxers do it as part of their training. It gets the heart beating fast and makes you very light on your feet.

A Closer Look at Skipping

Read the text carefully and circle the best answer to each question.

 1. Before 1900, skipping was
    a) mainly thought of as a girls' game.
    b) mainly thought of as a boys' game.
    c) unheard of.

 2. Skipping games before 1900
    a) were exactly the same as today.
    b) had not been invented.
    c) were simpler than they are today.

3. The songs and chants that children skip to today
    a) have been used for many years.
    b) have been used for only a few years.
    c) have been used for many centuries.

4. The words of the songs and chants
    a) remain the same.
    b) change a little.
    c) change completely every year.

 5. Athletes and boxers skip because
    a) they are very good at it.
    b) they like to sing the skipping songs.
    c) it is such good exercise.

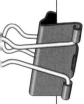

Find out for yourself

Write down any skipping rhymes you know. Try to find some more words of skipping rhymes, either from your own area or from other parts of the country. What differences are there?

Saving the Elephants

During the 1980s, African elephants suffered terribly, all because of human greed. It is estimated that more than 270 elephants were killed every day. The elephant population declined from over one million to around 600,000. So many adult elephants were killed that thousands of calves were orphaned.

Why would poachers want to kill these wonderful animals? They simply wanted their tusks for the ivory. Jewellery, knife handles, billiard balls and many other things have been made out of this beautiful, strong material.

Organisations that protect animals were outraged and launched a campaign. This led to an international ban on ivory sales in 1990, which did stop the decline in the elephant population. In some parts of Africa, however, poaching still goes on, so conservationists are continuing their campaign to protect the future of these wonderful animals.

Saving the Elephants

Read the text carefully and circle the best answer to each question.

 In this article, calves are
a) baby cows.
b) adult elephants.
c) baby elephants.

 During the 1980s
a) about 270 elephants were killed a day.
b) precisely 270 elephants were killed a day.
c) about 270 elephants were killed a week.

 A poacher is
a) someone who cooks eggs.
b) someone who kills animals for money.
c) someone who likes ivory.

 After selling ivory was made illegal in 1990, the number of elephants in Africa
a) continued to decrease.
b) stopped decreasing.
c) started to increase again.

 After it became illegal to sell ivory, some poachers
a) still killed elephants for their tusks.
b) became conservationists.
c) left Africa to poach in other countries.

Express yourself

Design a poster to help raise awareness of the plight of an endangered animal.

Where Are You?

① Serena and Jake are browsing. They don't see each other. Jake's shoulder pushes Serena against the shelves. Three volumes tumble to the floor with a loud thud. The woman behind the desk frowns and puts her index finger to her lips.

② Surrounded by bright lights, cold steel instruments and sterile surfaces, he breathed in the tense atmosphere of the life and death environment.

③ We are travelling at steady speed with only a monotonous 'clickety clack' to break the silence of the night.

④ The explorer moved cautiously through the swamps and thick vegetation, hoping to glimpse one of the rarest snakes in the world.

⑤ Floating weightlessly, the men and woman perform their routine tasks, the Earth appearing in the window behind as a bright blue ball.

Where Are You?

Read the text carefully and circle the best answer to each question.

 Where are they?
a) In a clothes shop.
b) In a museum.
c) In a library.

 Where was he?
a) In a cinema.
b) In an operating theatre.
c) On stage.

 Where are we?
a) On a train.
b) In a car.
c) On a plane.

 Where was she?
a) In the woods.
b) At the zoo.
c) In a rainforest.

 Where are they?
a) In space.
b) On a plane.
c) In a submarine.

Express yourself

Imagine yourself in one of these locations and write a story about what happened there.

Sightseeing in Europe: Italy

Venice

The Italian city of Venice is like no other city in the world. It is a city 'built on water'. In fact, it is built on dozens of small islands and criss-crossed by canals. The islands are joined by high arching footbridges.

The city has changed very little in 400 years and many of the old streets are extremely narrow and winding. Walking down one of the streets, you might find it coming to an abrupt halt at the water's edge, or opening onto a large town square.

There are no cars in Venice, but there is plenty of public transport. Instead of the usual buses and trains, however, there are boats. People get on and off by walking across wide floating platforms.

122

Venice

Read the text carefully and circle the best answer to each question.

 Venice is
a) a typical Italian city.
b) an unusual city.
c) the capital of Italy.

 In Venice, there are
a) more than 20 islands.
b) more than 12 islands.
c) exactly 12 islands.

 Venice is
a) a modern city.
b) at least 400 years old.
c) exactly 400 years old.

 There are no cars in Venice
a) so it is difficult to get around.
b) when the water is high.
c) but it is easy to get around.

 Public transport in Venice is
a) provided by boats.
b) provided by buses and trains.
c) non-existent.

Find out for yourself

Find out three more interesting facts about Venice.
Write another paragraph to add to this travel guide.

The Four Friends

There is an old story about four animals who were good friends. Unfortunately, instead of enjoying each other's company, they spent their days comparing themselves to one another, each wishing he was more like the other.

One day, the jungle genie appeared to them all in a swirl of green smoke.

'I'm fed up listening to your grumbling and groaning. You give me a headache every day. I have decided. I will grant you all one wish if you promise me you will stop complaining.'

The animals were delighted and each told the genie their wish.

'I wish my nose were smaller and not so grey,' said the first.

'I wish my legs were longer and not so scaly,' said the second.

'I wish my neck was shorter and not so blotchy,' said the third.

The fourth fluttered down from the tree and said wisely, 'Please make me happy with whoooooo I am.'

In a flash of blue lightning, their wishes were granted. The animals could no longer complain because they had promised the genie, but only one of them was happy.

The Four Friends

Read the text carefully and circle the best answer to each question.

 The four animals in the story
a) loved to be together.
b) didn't like each other.
c) were not happy with who they were.

 The first three animals were probably
a) a giraffe, an owl and an elephant.
b) an elephant, a giraffe and an alligator.
c) an elephant, a snake and a giraffe.

 The fourth animal was probably
a) an owl.
b) an ostrich.
c) an armadillo.

 Which of the animals was happy at the end?
a) The first.
b) The second.
c) The fourth.

 The message of the story is:
a) a genie can never make you happy.
b) accept who you are.
c) only some animals can be really happy.

Ask yourself

If you were given one wish, what would it be?
Think about it carefully to make sure that it
would really make you happy.

Bed and Breakfast
Archile Farmhouse

Sleeps 6

Near Fife

'Highly recommended'
Best of British B & B Guide

Relax and enjoy a real 'Taste of Scotland'. Our warm welcome and delicious, home-cooked food make this a very special place to stay. All three bedrooms have en-suite bathrooms, a colour television and a kettle with tea, coffee and homemade Scottish shortbread biscuits.

All our guests can also enjoy the comfortable lounge overlooking delightful gardens. Each evening, a four-course dinner is served in the elegant dining room.

At only an hour's drive from Edinburgh but in the heart of some of Scotland's most stunning scenery, you couldn't choose a better spot to stay.

Bed and Breakfast

Read the text carefully and circle the best answer to each question.

 1. The owners of this bed and breakfast
a) want to impress the reader.
b) want to put people off.
c) are very fussy.

 2. The homemade shortbread in each room
a) is bound to make crumbs on the carpet.
b) shows how much care they take looking after guests.
c) shows they have forgotten to buy them from the shop.

 3. The four-course dinner will be
a) bought from the local take-away.
b) a ready-meal from the supermarket.
c) cooked by the owners in their kitchen.

 4. The owners have written this description for
a) people who live in Scotland.
b) people who are visiting Scotland.
c) people moving house.

 5. The bed and breakfast is probably surrounded by
a) hills.
b) the sea.
c) busy streets.

Express yourself

Think about a time when you went on holiday or visited a place that is very different from where you live. Describe what it was like and how it was better or worse than what you were used to.

Wonder Wall

Have you ever seen pictures of the Earth taken from space? Astronauts often say how beautiful it looks.

From this huge distance you can see the blues and greens of the oceans and continents. You can see something else as well. It is a wiggly line across northern China. This is the Great Wall of China. It was built over hundreds of years by thousands of Chinese as protection from their enemies. Not surprisingly, parts of the wall have now crumbled, but some sections have been repaired.

Today the Great Wall of China is not needed for protection, but it is a huge attraction for tourists from all over the world. It is so popular that a company has been given special permission to collect loose pieces of stone from the wall and then sell them to visitors as souvenirs.

Wonder Wall

Fill in the gaps, choosing the best word or words from the text.

① _____ say the Earth is beautiful from space.

② From space, the Great Wall of China looks like a _____ .

③ The wall was built in the _____ part of China.

④ It was built by the Chinese to provide _____ from their enemies.

⑤ One _____ sells small pieces of the wall to tourists.

Ask yourself

Do you agree with the idea of selling bits of the Great Wall of China to tourists?
Explain the reasons for your answer.

People have always had teeth, but when did they first use toothbrushes? Today our toothbrushes are made out of nylon and plastic. These are modern materials, so what did people use before these were invented?

❖ 5,000 years ago, the Egyptians used a 'chew stick'. This was a twig with one end chewed until it was soft and frayed. As you chewed on the soft end, it cleaned your teeth.

❖ 500 years ago, the Chinese had toothbrushes with bamboo handles. The bristles were made from the hairs on the back of hogs' necks.

❖ 200 years ago, people in Europe used silver and brass toothpicks to pick out meat and other food stuck between their teeth. Poor people must have had cheaper toothpicks, made out of wood.

The nylon toothbrushes you are used to have been around for about 60 years.

You may have an electric toothbrush. These have only become available in the last 30 years. Who knows what we shall be using in another 30 years' time!

Smile!

Fill in the gaps, choosing the best word or words from the text.

1. Modern toothbrushes are made out of _____ and

   _____ .

2. 'Chew sticks' were used by the Egyptians _____ years

   ago.

3. Chinese toothbrushes had handles made out of _____ .

4. In Europe, 200 years ago, rich people had _____ made

   of silver and brass.

5. Electric toothbrushes have been around for _____ years.

Express yourself

Design a toothbrush of the future. What might it do that toothbrushes today can't? What will it look like? What will it be made out of? Let your imagination run away with you!

The Unicorn

There are many stories about this mysterious, mythical beast. With a body like a horse, a tail like a lion and a beard like a goat, the unicorn gets its name from the single horn that grows out from the middle of its forehead.

In the many myths told about the unicorn, the creature was said to be shy, living on its own in the forest. Its horn was thought to possess magical powers that could cure sickness. No hunter could ever catch the unicorn in the forest, however skilled he was. The unicorn was always faster and knew the secrets of the forest. But, if a beautiful girl went into the forest and sat down by a lake, the unicorn would come and lay its head in her lap.

The Unicorn

Fill in the gaps, choosing the best word or words from the text.

① The unicorn is said to have a beard like a _____ .

② It has one _____ growing out of its forehead.

③ The unicorn's horn was thought to be a _____ for sickness.

④ It was impossible even for a skilled _____ to catch the unicorn.

⑤ The unicorn would lay its head in the lap of a _____ .

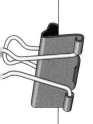

Find out for yourself
See what else you can find out about the unicorn.

Two Airlifted from Drifting Yacht

Helicopter crews from an RAF base rescued two injured crew members from a British yacht stranded 480 miles from the coast of Land's End today. Their 64-foot yacht had been damaged by stormy weather.

In a dramatic dawn rescue, the two injured men were airlifted by Sikorsky CH-3E helicopters from a nearby RAF station. The yacht had been travelling from the Caribbean to the UK when it ran into high seas and gales south west of Land's End. It is thought that both the sailors have broken ribs. The rest of the crew remained on board to make their way to port.

Two Airlifted from Drifting Yacht

Fill in the gaps, choosing the best word or words from the text.

① The rescue was made by _____ helicopter crews.

② The British yacht was _____ from land.

③ Sikorsky _____ helicopters came from an RAF base.

④ The yacht had run into difficulty _____ off Land's End.

⑤ The injured men may have broken _____ .

Express yourself

Imagine that you are one of the injured sailors.
Write a diary account of the rescue.

THE FAIRY RING

You might have seen toadstools growing in a circle in the grass. This is called a 'fairy ring'. It used to be said that when the moon shone, fairies would dance inside the ring to beautiful music. Legend has it that if a human steps inside the ring to dance with the fairies, a terrible thing will happen. For every minute that they spend inside the ring, they will grow seven years older.

One story tells what happened to a young man called Shon. One night he was enchanted by the fairies' music and stepped inside the ring to dance with them. After a while he tried to go, but the fairies would not let him leave their dance. At last he crawled to the edge and managed to put his finger outside the ring. The spell was broken and he ran home.

He knocked at his door. Instead of his wife, an old man answered.

'Who are you?' said the old man.

'I'm Shon. Where are my wife and son?'

'Shon was my grandfather. He went away when my grandmother was young. He never came back.'

The truth hit Shon. The minutes he had spent in the fairy ring had made him an old man. Years had passed and his family were dead.

The Fairy Ring

Fill in the gaps, choosing the best word or words from the text.

① A fairy ring is made up of lots of _____ .

② Legend has it that for every minute spent inside a fairy ring, a human

ages by _____ years.

③ The fairy music _____ Shon so that he wanted to dance.

④ Shon broke the _____ by putting his finger outside

the ring.

⑤ The old man who answered the door said that Shon was his

_____ .

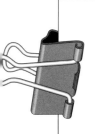

Express yourself

Write the story, imagining that you are Shon.
Describe how you felt on returning home. What did
you do next?

Amazing Mozart

When he was just five years old, Wolfgang Amadeus Mozart could play music better than most grown-ups.

Mozart was born in Salzberg, Austria, in the 1700s. His father was a musician and taught him music as soon as he could talk. At three, Wolfgang could play the harpsichord (an instrument like a piano) and when he was six he picked up a violin. Although he had never had a lesson, he could play it perfectly.

Wolfgang's father realised how gifted his son was. He decided to take him around Europe so that people could hear his son play. Wolfgang played for kings and queens in many different countries. People were astonished at how he could play music he had never even seen before.

He started to compose music when he was just five. One of these early pieces was variations on 'Twinkle, Twinkle, Little Star'. By the time he was ten he had written five symphonies. Mozart spent much of his adult life composing. He wrote 36 symphonies and many shorter pieces of music. Today his music is loved and performed all over the world.

Amazing Mozart

Fill in the gaps, choosing the best word or words from the text.

〈1〉 Mozart was born in the Austrian city of _____ .

〈2〉 Wolfgang's father took him to play for people all round

_____ .

〈3〉 When he was _____ , Wolfgang composed his first piece
of music.

〈4〉 He had written five _____ before he was ten.

〈5〉 His music is still being _____ today.

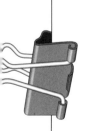

Find out for yourself

Mozart wrote lots of symphonies and concertos.
What is the difference between a symphony and a
concerto? See if you can find either a symphony or
a concerto by Mozart and listen to some of it.

The Miracle Mould

Nowadays, if we have a bad sore throat or a wound that has become infected, a doctor will give us some medicine called an 'antibiotic'. It's hard to believe that less than a hundred years ago this sort of medicine was not available and that people with sore throats and cuts often died from their illness.

A Scottish doctor called Alexander Fleming made a discovery that was to save countless lives. At that time, many people were dying because there was no way of killing the harmful germs in their bodies. Fleming was investigating the germs by growing them in dishes of special 'soup'. When the soup was full of germs, it was cloudy; when there were no germs, the soup was clear. One day, Fleming found some mould growing on one of the dishes. Thinking the investigation was ruined, he was about to throw it away. Then he noticed that although the soup in the dish was cloudy with germs, all around the mould it was clear. Something in the mould must have killed the germs!

Fleming was very excited. If he could find out what it was in the mould that killed the germs, he could use it to make medicine. After 12 years of work, Alexander Fleming had developed penicillin, an antibiotic that is still used today.

The Miracle Mould

Fill in the gaps, choosing the best word or words from the text.

1. Doctors use _____ medicines to treat illness such as sore throats.

2. Alexander Fleming was an _____ doctor.

3. When Fleming's special soup was cloudy, he knew there were _____ in it.

4. Fleming thought that there might be something in the _____ that could kill germs.

5. It was 12 more years before the medicine called _____ was available for medical use.

Express yourself

Imagine you are Alexander Fleming. Write up your diary entry for the day when you discovered the mould in the soup.

Fill in each gap, choosing the best word or words from the list of possible answer

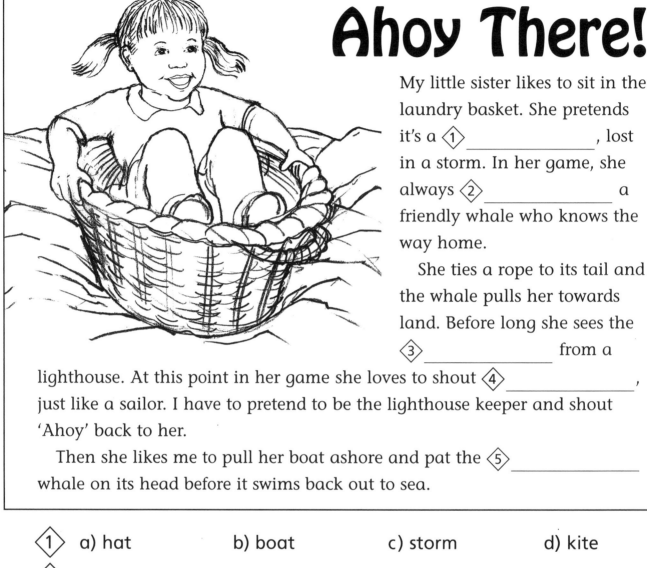

Ahoy There!

My little sister likes to sit in the laundry basket. She pretends it's a ①_____, lost in a storm. In her game, she always ②_____ a friendly whale who knows the way home.

She ties a rope to its tail and the whale pulls her towards land. Before long she sees the ③_____ from a lighthouse. At this point in her game she loves to shout ④_____, just like a sailor. I have to pretend to be the lighthouse keeper and shout 'Ahoy' back to her.

Then she likes me to pull her boat ashore and pat the ⑤_____ whale on its head before it swims back out to sea.

① a) hat   b) boat   c) storm   d) kite

② a) forgets   b) loses   c) meets   d) annoys

③ a) fog   b) steam   c) music   d) light

④ a) 'Ahoy'   b) 'Goodbye'   c) 'Hi'   d) 'Get lost'

⑤ a) scary   b) friendly   c) mean   d) shy

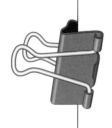

Express yourself

Were there any pretend games you liked to play over and over again when you were younger? Write down what you did and why you liked it so much.

ll in each gap, choosing the best word or words from the list of possible answers.

Jam Tarts

Ingredients

100g plain flour

pinch of ①_____

1 teaspoon sugar

25g softened lard

25g softened butter

cold water

jam

Method

Sift the flour into a large ②_____ bowl, then add the sugar. Chop up the fat and rub it into the flour with your fingers. Add the water and knead the dough together. Roll out the ③_____ and use a round cutter to press out the pastry cases. Grease a tin and put a pastry circle into each hole. Add 1 heaped teaspoon of jam, not too ④_____ or it will flow over the top. Bake for 20–25 minutes, gas mark 5, 190° C. Leave to cool on a wire ⑤_____ .

① a) pasta   b) salt   c) flesh   d) milk

② a) chopping   b) spinning   c) mixing   d) dog

③ a) jam   b) flour   c) fat   d) pastry

④ a) much   b) little   c) quietly   d) quickly

⑤ a) fence   b) rack   c) plate   d) oven

Find out for yourself

Find out about other types of pastry and how you make them.

Fill in each gap, choosing the best word or words from the list of possible answer

Platypus

Ornithorhynchus anatinus

Australia is 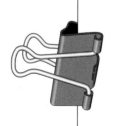① _____ to many unusual and interesting animals. The kangaroo, the koala and the platypus are probably the most ② _____. The platypus is unusual because it is an egg-laying mammal. It can be ③ _____ in fresh water in parts of eastern Australia. It has a rubbery bill and velvety fur in shades of dark brown to yellow. It has a long, flat tail and webbed feet that allow it to swim well ④ _____. The hind feet of the male platypus each have a spur filled with venom that can kill some small animals or ⑤ _____ larger ones.

Walchester Zoo

①   a) far away   b) home   c) hot   d) strange

②   a) wild   b) well known   c) rare   d) poisonous

③   a) lost   b) lonely   c) found   d) captured

④   a) under water   b) on land   c) in the pool   d) alone

⑤   a) tickle   b) deafen   c) injure   d) kill

Ask yourself

Probably your only chance to see animals such as the platypus or the kangaroo is at the zoo. What do you think about keeping such animals in captivity? Explain the reasons for your answer.

ll in each gap, choosing the best word or words from the list of possible answers.

Tsunami

I'm sure you know about earthquakes. They are caused by large sections of the Earth's ⟨1⟩ _____ moving against each other. But have you heard of a tsunami? These natural disasters are not as well known, but are just as dramatic as earthquakes.

So what is a ⟨2⟩ _____ ? It is an enormous wave, which can be caused by an underwater earthquake, a landslide or an erupting volcano. These colossal walls of water can reach a height of over 30 metres. Some scientists in Japan have become tsunami ⟨3⟩ _____ .

These scientists are able to find out when and where the ⟨4⟩ _____ earthquakes are happening. They have created something called the Pacific Tsunami Warning System. The system detects when and where underwater earthquakes are going to happen so that the wave does not take ⟨5⟩ _____ by surprise. It is hoped that lives and property can be protected.

⟨1⟩ a) atmosphere   b) crust   c) bottom   d) water
⟨2⟩ a) earthquake   b) volcano   c) tsunami   d) landslide
⟨3⟩ a) victims   b) followers c) teachers   d) experts
⟨4⟩ a) underwater   b) tiny   c) best   d) important
⟨5⟩ a) fish   b) people   c) scientists d) surfers

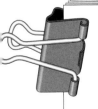

Express yourself
Write a poem about a tsunami.

Fill in each gap, choosing the best word or words from the list of possible answer

The Fable of the Wise Monkey and the Ogre

There was once a magical forest in India. The ⟨1⟩ _____ was beautiful, with a large, cool lake, but if any animal tried to drink from it, an ogre would jump out and eat them.

The animals were so ⟨2⟩ _____, they didn't know what to do. One day a wise old monkey came to the water's edge. He leant over it to see what would happen. The other animals watched, terrified. Before long, the ⟨3⟩ _____ head of the ogre appeared from out of the water.

'Come and drink, Old Monkey,' he said, 'the water is cool and refreshing.'

'No, I won't,' said the Monkey, 'You will eat me. I would rather be thirsty than ⟨4⟩ _____.'

'But this is the only water in the forest. You will have to drink sooner or later. I will be waiting for you.'

The Old Monkey looked around and saw some long hollow reeds growing next to the lake. He picked the reeds and gave them to all the animals. The ogre was furious when he saw the animals ⟨5⟩ _____ the water through the reeds. No animal was ever eaten by him again.

⟨1⟩ a) magic   b) forest   c) lake   d) ogre

⟨2⟩ a) hungry   b) wise   c) thirsty   d) lazy

⟨3⟩ a) hideous   b) cute   c) wet   d) delicate

⟨4⟩ a) wet   b) hungry   c) dead   d) asleep

⟨5⟩ a) slurping   b) sucking   c) blowing   d) tasting

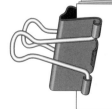

Express yourself

Make up your own fable about a wise animal. Think about which animals are thought of as wise and why that might be.

ll in each gap, choosing the best word or words from the list of possible answers.

Free-flying Frisbee

Vhy is a frisbee called a ①_____?

n the 1870s, there was a baker who ved in Connecticut, USA. He sold his ies in tins that were embossed with is family ②_____. His ame was William Russell Frisbie.

tudents, who went to nearby Yale niversity, bought his ③_____. hey used to play games with the mpty tins, throwing them to each ther across the college lawns.

ears later, in the 1950s, a man called Valter Frederick Morrison made a toy hat was meant to look like a UFO. It vas called a 'Flyin' Saucer'. To begin vith it was made out of metal, but vas later changed to ④_____.

The toy company that sold the Flyin' Saucers found out that students at university were still throwing William Frisbie's metal pie tins around. They decided to rename their toy the 'Frisbee', changing the ⑤_____ by just one letter.

---

①	a) hula hoop	b) frisbee	c) pie tin	d) flying saucer
②	a) name	b) dog	c) shop	d) home
③	a) meat	b) shop	c) pies	d) frisbees
④	a) wood	b) silver	c) paper	d) plastic
⑤	a) spelling	b) letters	c) address	d) material

Find out for yourself

Choose another well-known toy and try to find out where and how it was invented.

Fill in each gap, choosing the best word or words from the list of possible answer

RECORD-BREAKING BUBBLES

People hold records for the strangest things! For instance, a girl called Susan Williams holds the record for ①_____ the largest bubble-gum bubble. It was nearly 70 cm in diameter. ②_____ what a mess it made when it burst!

Other people have also puffed their way to world records. Some students in the Netherlands set a record by combining their lung capacity with their ③_____ ability. They used 25,344 inflated balloons to imitate a famous Van Gogh painting of fishing boats on a beach.

Alan McKay made the record books for making a huge ④_____ bubble. He used an especially large bubble wand, lots of dishwashing liquid and glycerine. His soap bubble was a ⑤_____ 222 metres across.

Have you got any ideas for a world record?

 a) eating   b) blowing   c) bursting   d) inventing

 a) Pretend   b) Explain   c) Imagine   d) Describe

 a) artistic   b) sporting   c) natural   d) unusual

 a) ice cream   b) soap   c) glass   d) plastic

 a) colossal   b) puny   c) mere   d) disappointin

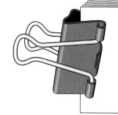

Find out for yourself

Find out about some more world records and list the five that you think are the most unusual.

Fill in each gap, choosing the best word or words from the list of possible answers.

WATER MOUSE BOATS FOR HIRE

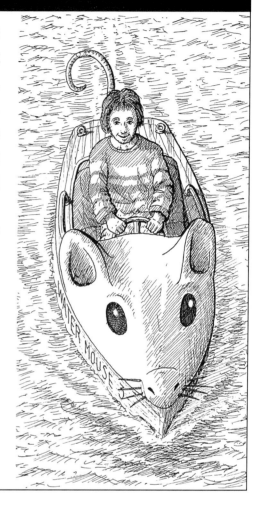

At the **BIG SPLASH HOTEL**, we do everything we can to make sure 1 _____ have a great holiday, just like their parents. Strictly for the kids, this summer we have our new fleet of Water Mice. The Water Mouse is a speedy little boat that gives hours of fun on the pleasure lake. And if you are 10 or 2 _____ , you can take the controls all by yourself! You can be sure of a splashing time!

   But don't take our word for it – here are some of our satisfied customers' views.

   'It's 3 _____ *! I was turning into the waves and they splashed right over me.'* Darius Lambert, aged 9

   'It's exciting to be in charge of your own 4 _____ *. I'm definitely gonna do it again!'* Elspeth Freer, aged 12

You can 5 _____ a Water Mouse from the hotel pleasure lake at just $18 for half an hour.

1	a) grown-ups	b) fuss-pots	c) kids	d) grannies
2	a) older	b) under	c) 20	d) bigger
3	a) terrible	b) amazing	c) wet	d) scary
4	a) car	b) life	c) boat	d) ride
5	a) buy	b) hire	c) steal	d) borrow

Express yourself

Imagine you are riding on a Water Mouse when, suddenly, it seems to take on a life of its own and you can no longer control it. What happens next?

Answers

Getting the main idea

Body Art
1) c.　2) b.　3) a.　4) a.　5) c.

Tricks and Illusions
1) a.　2) b.　3) a.　4) c.　5) a.

Under the Bed
1) b.　2) c.　3) a.　4) b.　5) a.

Yo-yos
1) c.　2) b.　3) a.　4) a.　5) c.

Red Kangaroo
1) a.　2) c.　3) b.　4) a.　5) b.

Merlin's Treasures
1) c.　2) a.　3) b.　4) c.　5) a.

Reptile Relatives
1) a.　2) b.　3) c.　4) c.　5) a.

A Peeling Poem
1) b.　2) a.　3) c.　4) a.　5) b.

A Good Day for the Princess
1) b.　2) a.　3) c.　4) b.　5) a.

Making inferences

Lucy and Tom
1) a.　2) c.　3) a.　4) b.　5) c.

We Are Not Amused
1) b.　2) a.　3) c.　4) b.　5) a.

Surprise
1) b.　2) c.　3) a.　4) b.　5) c.

A Closer Look at Skipping
1) b.　2) c.　3) a.　4) b.　5) c.

Save the Elephants
1) c.　2) a.　3) b.　4) b.　5) a.

Where Are You?
1) c.　2) b.　3) a.　4) c.　5) a.

Venice
1) b.　2) a.　3) b.　4) c.　5) a.

The Four Friends
1) c.　2) b.　3) a.　4) c.　5) b.

Bed and Breakfast
1) a.　2) b.　3) c.　4) b.　5) a.

Noting details

Wonder Wall
1) Astronauts
2) wiggly line
3) northern
4) protection
5) company

Smile!
1) nylon, plastic
2) 5,000
3) bamboo
4) toothpicks
5) 30

The Unicorn
1) goat
2) horn
3) cure
4) hunter
5) beautiful girl

Two Airlifted from Drifting Yacht
1) RAF
2) 480 miles
3) CH-3E
4) south west
5) ribs

The Fairy Ring
1) toadstools
2) seven
3) enchanted
4) spell
5) grandfather

Amazing Mozart
1) Salzberg
2) Europe
3) five
4) symphonies
5) performed

The Miracle Mould
1) antibiotic
2) English
3) germs
4) mould
5) penicillin

Using context clues

Ahoy There!
1) b.　2) c.　3) d.　4) a.　5) b.

Jam Tarts
1) b.　2) c.　3) d.　4) a.　5) b.

Platypus
1) b.　2) b.　3) c.　4) a.　5) c.

Tsunami
1) b.　2) c.　3) d.　4) a.　5) b.

The Fable of the Wise Monkey and the Ogre
1) b.　2) c.　3) a.　4) c.　5) b.

Free-flying Frisbee
1) b.　2) a.　3) c.　4) d.　5) a.

Record-breaking Bubbles
1) b.　2) c.　3) a.　4) b.　5) a.

Water Mouse Boats for Hire
1) c.　2) a.　3) b.　4) c.　5) b.